BRENTWOOD-BENSON MUSIC P

TOP ANTHEMS volume 3

15 BEST-SELLING SONGS FROM TODAY'S LEADING ARRANGERS

Compiled and Created by Johnathan Crumpton & Luke Gambill

AVAILABLE PRODUCTS:

PHYSICAL PRODUCTS

Choral Book	45757-2804-7
CD Preview Pak	45757-2804-1
Listening CD (2 Discs)	45757-2804-2
Split-Track Accompaniment CD (2 Discs)	45757-2804-3
Audio Stem Files	45757-2804-4
Orchestration/Conductor's Score CD-Rom	45757-2804-8
Soprano Rehearsal Track CD (2 Discs)	45757-2805-0
Alto Rehearsal Track CD (2 Discs)	45757-2805-5
Tenor Rehearsal Track CD (2 Discs)	45757-2805-6
Bass Rehearsal Track CD (2 Discs)	45757-2805-7

DIGITAL DOWNLOAD PRODUCTS

Digital Choral Book – SATB/Vocal Only (PDF Download)	45757-2846-6
Digital Choral Book – Piano/SATB (PDF Download)	45757-2846-7
Digital Orchestration/Conductor's Score (PDF Download)	45757-2846-8
Digital Listening Tracks (MP3 Download)	45757-2846-2
Digital Split-Track Accompaniments (MP3 Download)	45757-2846-3
Digital Audio Stem Files (MP3 Download)	45757-2846-4

INSTRUMENTATION:

Flute 1,2 • Oboe • Clarinet 1,2 • F Horn 1,2 (Alto Sax) • Trumpet 1,2 • Trumpet 3 • Trombone 1,2 (Tenor Sax/Baritone T.C.) Trombone 3,4 • Percussion • Harp • Violin 1 • Violin 2 • Viola • Cello • Bass • Synth String Reduction • Rhythm

BRENTWOOD-BENSON music publications

www.brentwoodbenson.com

Contents

Here at the Cross

Words and Music by
DAVID MOFFITT, SUE C. SMITH
and JASON DYBA
Arranged by Cliff Duren

15
ev - er. Here at the cross where the
C♯m B E F♯m/E E E E/G♯
18
blind re - ceive their sight. How the nails have pierced my
A A/C♯ Bsus B C♯m B/D♯ E
21
heart and I bow in glad sur - ren - der.
A2 C♯m E/G♯ A E/B B

24
Here at the cross where my Je - sus bled and
E F♯m/E E E E/G♯ A B
27
died.
DISC 1 3
E A/E E E A/E E
31
Here where the cry of the Sav - ior splits the
E F♯m/E E E E/G♯ A E/G♯

34
dark - ness. Here where His life is so
C♯m B E F♯m/E E E E/G♯
37
mf
frag-ile, yet di - vine. It's the won - der of His
A A/C♯ Bsus B C♯m B/D♯ E
mf
40
grace and the love that I re - mem - ber.
A2 C♯m E/G♯ A2 E/B B

43
mp
Here ___ at the cross, it's re - demp - tion that ___ I
E F♯m/E E E E/G♯ A2 B
mp
46
find.
DISC 1 4
E A/E E F B♭/F
mf
49
mf
Here I am free, al - though
F C7sus F Gm/F F F F/A

52
once a slave, now res - cued. Here I am
B♭ F/A Dm C F Gm/F
55
strong, al-though once in grav - est plight. And the
F F F/A B♭ B♭/D Csus C
58
trea - sure of His love mak-ing rich the help - less
Dm C/E F B♭2 Dm F/A B♭2

61
unis.
beg - gar. Here I am clean and the crim-son stain now
F/C C F Gm/F F F F/A B♭2 C F/C C
65
white.
Dm C/E F B♭2 Dm F/A B♭2 F/C C
f
69
DISC 1
5
F B♭/F F F B♭/F F
mp

73
mp
Here at the cross with for - give - ness of - fered free - ly.
F(no3)
B♭2/F
C/F
p
77
mf cresc.
Here where the Lamb o - pens wide sal - va - tion's
Dm
C/E
F
B♭2
mp
80
f
door. All my past is burned a - way, glo - ry
Csus
C
Dm
C/E
F
B♭2
f

83
ris - ing from the em - bers. Here at the
Dm F/A B♭2 F/C C F Gm/F
86
DISC 1 6
unis.
cross, praise His name for - ev - er - more.
F F F/A B♭2 C F Fsus/G F/A Fsus/G F C/E
89
Here at the cross, praise His name for -
Dm C/E F F F/A B♭ C Dm

DISC 1
7
92
molto rit.
ev - er more!
Csus C F
molto rit.
Broader (♩=65)
95
ff
Here at the cross, called the hum - ble Man of
G♭ A♭m/G♭ G♭ G♭ G♭/B♭ C♭ G♭/B♭
ff Broader (♩=65)
98
Sor - rows. Up from the grave, see Him
E♭m D♭ G♭ A♭m/G♭ G♭ G♭ G♭/B♭

101
rise, oh glo - rious morn. Now in pow - er He as-
C♭ C♭/E♭ D♭sus D♭ E♭m D♭/F G♭
104
cends, robed in maj - es - ty and splen - dor;
C♭2 G♭ G♭/F E♭m G♭/B♭ C♭2 G♭/D♭ D♭
107
DISC 1
8
reign - ing on high, King of kings and Lord of
G♭ A♭m/G♭ G♭ G♭ G♭/B♭ C♭2 D♭

110
lords. Now in pow - er He as - cends, robed in
G♭ G♭/F E♭m D♭/F G♭ C♭2 G♭ G♭/F
113
maj - es - ty and splen - dor; reign - ing on
E♭m G♭/B♭ C♭2 G♭/D♭ D♭ G♭ A♭m/G♭
116
DISC 1
9
high, King of kings and Lord of lords.
G♭ G♭ G♭/B♭ C♭2 D♭ G♭ G♭sus/A♭ G♭/B♭ G♭sus/A♭ G♭ D♭/F

119
Reign - ing on high, King of kings and
E♭m D♭ D♭sus/E♭ D♭/F G♭ G♭ G♭/B♭ C♭ D♭ E♭m
DISC 1
10
122
unis.
Lord of lords! King of
unis.
D♭sus D♭ G♭ A♭m/G♭ G♭ D♭/F E♭m7 G♭/D♭
125
molto rit.
kings and Lord of lords!
C♭ E♭m D♭sus D♭ G♭

10,000 Reasons (Bless the Lord)

Words and Music by
JONAS MYRIN and MATT REDMAN
Arranged by Cliff Duren

14
Wor-ship His ho - ly name. Sing like nev-er be-fore,
G D Asus A G Bm
17
DISC 1
13
O my soul. I wor-ship Your ho - ly name.
G A Bm7 G2 A G/D D
20
The sun comes up. It's a new day dawn - ing.
G/D A/D D G D A Bm7

23
It's time to sing Your song a - gain. What-
G D A Bm7
25
ev - er may pass and what - ev - er lies be - fore me,
G D A/C♯ Bm7
27
DISC 1 14
let me be sing-ing when the ev - 'ning comes.
G2 D Asus A D G/D

30
mf
unis.
Bless the Lord, O my soul, O my soul.
unis.
D G D A/C♯ Bm
mf
33
Wor-ship His ho - ly name.
Sing like
G D Asus A
35
decresc.
nev - er be-fore, O my soul. I wor-ship Your ho - ly name.
G Bm7 G A Bm7 G A
decresc.

DISC 1
15
38
mp unis.
You're rich in love, and You're
unis.
G/D D G/D A/D D G D
mp
41
slow to an - ger. Your name is great, and Your heart is kind. For
A Bm G D A Bm7
44
all Your good-ness I will keep on sing - ing;
G D A/C♯ Bm7

DISC 1 16
46
cresc.
ten thou-sand rea-sons for my heart to find.
G D Asus A G D
49
f
unis.
Bless the Lord, O my soul, O my soul.
unis.
A/C# Bm D/A G D A/C# Bm
52
Wor-ship His ho - ly name. Sing like nev-er be-fore,
G D Asus A G Bm7

55
unis.
O my soul. I wor-ship Your ho - ly name.
G A Bm7 G A(no3) G Bm
f
DISC 1
17
58
mp
And
unis.
G A Bm D/A G2
61
on that day when my strength is fail-ing, the end draws near and my
G D A Bm7 G D
mp

64
time has come, still my soul will sing Your praise un -
A Bm7 G D A
67
mf (more gutsy tone)
end - ing; ten thou-sand years and then for - ev - er -
Bm7 G D Asus A
70
DISC 1
18
f
more! Bless the
D G/D D(no3) D/F♯
mf

72
unis.
Lord, O my soul, O my soul. Wor-ship His ho - ly name.
G D A/C♯ Bm G D
f
75
DISC 1 19
1.
unis.
Sing like nev - er be-fore, O my soul. I
Asus A G Bm7
1.
G A Bm7
78
(page 24, meas. 72)
2.
wor-ship Your ho - ly name. Bless the O my soul. I
(page 24, meas. 72)
2.
G A(no3) G/D D D/F♯ G A Bm7

DISC 1
20
81
worship Your holy name. I
G
A(no3)
Bm
83
mp unis.
worship Your holy name. I
unis.
G
A
Bm
85
worship Your holy name.
G
A
G
D
A/C♯
Bm
mp

DISC 1 21

88
mp
Sing like nev - er be-fore,
G D Asus A G Bm

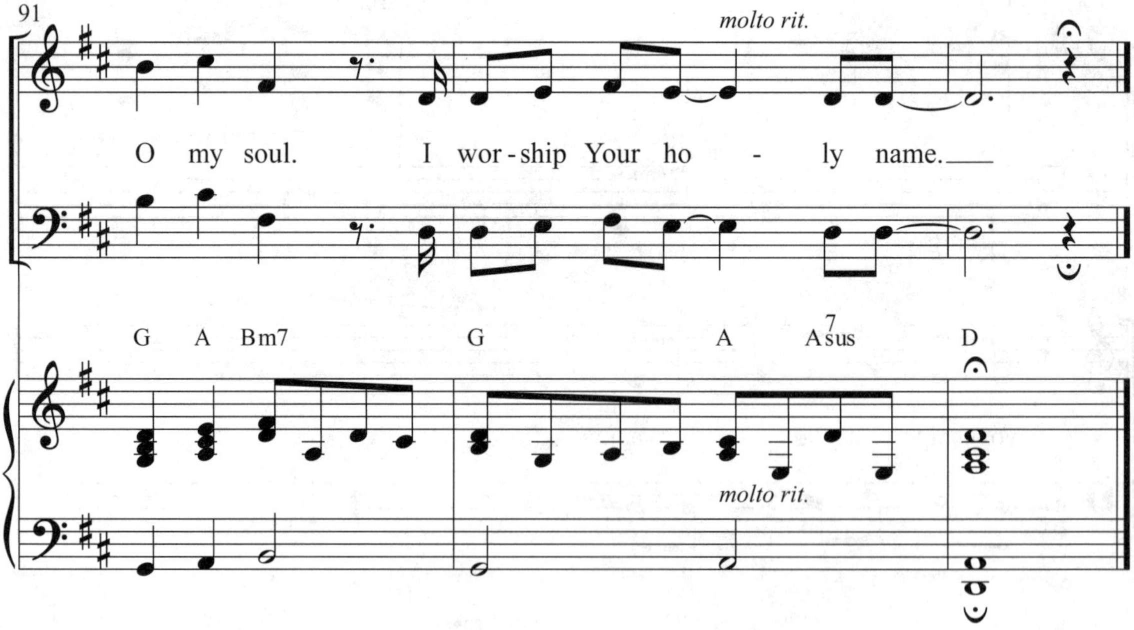
91
molto rit.
O my soul. I wor-ship Your ho - ly name.
G A Bm7 G A A7sus D
molto rit.

We Will Remember

Words and Music by
TOMMY WALKER
Arranged by Bradley Knight

9
We will stop and give You praise, for
D
D7/F♯
G
DISC 1 23
DISC 1 24
11
1. (page 27, meas. 5)
2.
great is Thy faith - ful - ness.
D/A
G/A
N.C.
D E D B A
14
SOLO
You're our Cre - a - tor, our life Sus - tain - er,
D
G/D

16
De - liv - er - er, our Com - fort, our Joy.
D/F♯
Bm
A
18
Through-out the a - ges, You've been our Shel - ter, our
D
G
20
DISC 1
25
Peace in the midst of the storm.
D/A
G/A
D
G
D/F♯
Em7

22
DUET
With signs and won - ders, You've shown Your pow - er.
D
G/D
24
With prec - ious blood, You showed us Your grace.
D/F♯
Bm
A
26
You've been our Help - er, our Lib - er - a - tor, the
D
D/F♯
G

DISC 1
26
28
Giv - er of life with no end.
D/A G/A D G D/F♯ N.C. E D B A
30
CHOIR
mf
SOLOIST may ad lib
We will re - mem - ber,
we will re - mem - ber,
D G
mf
32
we will re - mem - ber the works of Your hands.
D D A/C♯ Bm A

34
We will stop and give You praise, for
D
D7
F♯
G
Em7
36
DISC 1
27
great is Thy faith - ful - ness.
D
A
G
A
D
N.C.
E D B A
38
mp
unis.
When we walk through life's dark-est val - leys,
unis.
D
G
D
mp

40
we will look back at all You have done.
D/F♯
Bm
A
42
f
And we will shout, "Our God is good, and
D
D7/F♯
G
Em7
f
DISC 1
28
44
He is the faith - ful One."
D/A
G/A
D

46
Hal - le - lu - jah! Hal - le - lu - jah! to the
A A Bm D/F♯
48
One from whom all bless - ings flow.
G D/F♯ Asus A E/G♯ A
50
Hal - le - lu - jah! Hal - le - lu - jah! to the
A A Bm D/F♯

DISC 1
29
52
One whose glo - ry has been shown.
G
D/F♯
Asus
B♭sus
54
f
We will re - mem - ber,
we will re - mem - ber,
E♭
A♭
f
56
we will re - mem - ber the works of Your hands.
E♭
E♭
B♭/D
Cm
B♭

58
We will stop and give You praise, for
E♭
E♭7/G
A♭
Fm7
60
great is Thy faith - ful - ness.
E♭/B♭
A♭/B♭
E♭
E♭7
mf
DISC 1
30
62
A♭/E♭
E♭
E♭7
A♭/E♭

65
SOLO
mp
I still re-mem-ber the day You saved me,
E♭
A♭/E♭
mp
67
the day I heard You call out my name.
E♭/G
Cm
B♭
DISC 1
31
69
CHOIR
f
You said You loved me, would nev-er leave me, and
E♭
E♭7/G
A♭
Fm7
E♭/G
Fm/A♭
Fm

71
I've nev - er been the same!
Eb/Bb
Ab/Bb
Eb
Ab
Eb/G
Fm7
73
We will re - mem - ber,
we will re - mem - ber,
Eb
Ab
75
we will re - mem - ber the works of Your hands.
Eb
Eb
Bb/D
Cm
Bb

77
We will stop and give You praise, for
E♭
E♭7/G
A♭
Fm7
79
DISC 1
32
great is Thy faith - ful - ness.
E♭/B♭
A♭/B♭
E♭
B♭/C
81
We will re - mem - ber,
we will re - mem - ber,
F
B♭

83
we will re - mem - ber the works of Your hands.
F
F C/E Dm7 C
DISC 1
33
85
We will stop and give You praise, for
F F Gm7 F/A F B♭ Gm7
87
rit.
great is Thy faith - ful - ness. A - men!
F/C B♭/C F B♭ F/A Gm7 F
rit.

Praise the Father, Praise the Son

Words and Music by
CHRIS TOMLIN and ED CASH
Arranged by Cliff Duren

14
dore, the an - gels sing, and fall be - fore the throne of
B♭/D
E♭
DISC 1
36
17
grace. To You be - longs the high - est praise.
Gm7
Cm7
Fsus
B♭
B♭sus
20
ALL
These suf - fer - ings, this pass - ing tide un - der Your
B♭
B♭
E♭/B♭
B♭

23
wings I will a - bide, and ev - 'ry en - e - my shall
B♭/D
E♭
DISC 1
37
26
flee. You are my hope and vic - to - ry.
Gm7
Cm7
Fsus
B♭
B♭sus
29
mf
Praise the Fa - ther, praise the Son, praise the
B♭
B♭/D
E♭2
F7sus
B♭
B♭/D
mf

32
Spir - it, Three in One. Clothed in pow - er and in
E♭2 F♯° Gm7 B♭/D E♭2 F7sus
35
decresc.
unis.
grace; the Name a - bove all oth - er names.
unis.
B♭ Cm7 Fsus B♭ B♭sus
38
DISC 1
38
B♭ B♭ B♭sus

40
mf
To the val - ley, for my soul; Thy great de -
B♭ B♭ E♭/B♭ B♭
mf
43
scent has made me whole. Your Word my heart has wel-comed
B♭/D B♭maj7/D E♭
46
unis.
DISC 1
39
cresc.
home; now peace like wa - ter ev - er flows. Praise the
Gm7 Cm7 Fsus B♭ B♭/D

49
building 2nd time
Fa - ther, praise the Son, praise the Spir - it, Three in
E♭2 F7sus B♭ B♭/D E♭2 F♯°
building 2nd time
52
unis.
One. Clothed in pow - er and in grace; the Name a -
Gm7 B♭/D E♭2 F7sus B♭
55
1.
(page 46, meas. 49)
2.
bove all oth - er names. Praise the bove all oth - er
Cm7 Fsus B♭ B♭/D Cm7 Fsus

DISC 1 40
58
f
names! Yours is the
B♭ B♭sus B♭
f
61
King - dom. Yours is the pow - er.
F(add4) Gm7 E♭2
64
DISC 1 41
Yours is the glo - ry for - ev -
B♭ F(add4) E♭2

67
er! Yours is the King - dom.
F
B♭
F(add4)
70
Yours is the pow - er. Yours is the
Gm7
E♭2
B♭
73
DISC 1
42
glo - ry for - ev - er!
F(add4)
E♭2
F

76
ff rit.
a tempo
Praise the Fa - ther, praise the Son, praise the
G7sus
C/E
F2
G7sus
C
C/E
rit.
ff a tempo
79
Spir - it, Three in One. Clothed in pow - er and in
F2
G#°
Am7
C/E
F2
G7sus
82
DISC 1
43
2nd time
unis.
1.
(page 49, meas. 77)
grace; the Name a - bove all oth - er names. Praise the
C
Dm7
Gsus
C
C/E

85
2.
bove all oth-er names. The Name a - bove all oth-er
2.
Dm7 Gsus C Em7 F2 Gsus
88
names. The Name a - bove all oth - er names!
C C/E F2 Gsus C Csus
92
rit.
C Csus C
rit.

Just as I Am (I Come Broken)

CHARLOTTE ELLIOTT

WILLIAM B. BRADBURY
Additional Lyrics by TRAVIS COTTRELL,
DAVID MOFFITT and SUE C. SMITH
Arranged by Travis Cottrell

7
out one plea but that Thy blood was
wait - ing not to rid my soul of
B♭sus
B♭2
F/B♭
E♭2/B♭
11
shed for me, and that Thou bidst me
one dark blot. To Thee whose blood can
F/B♭
B♭2
B♭2/A
15
come to Thee, O Lamb of God, I
cleanse each spot, O Lamb of God, I
Gm7(4)
E♭2
B♭2/D
E♭2

DISC 1 45
DISC 1 46
19
1.
(page 51, meas. 5)
come, I come.
come, I
Just
Fsus
F
B♭2
B♭sus
23
2.
come.
I come bro - ken to be
B♭2
B♭2/A
Gm7
26
mend - ed. I come wound - ed to be healed. I come

29
des - perate to be res - cued. I come emp - ty to be
Gm7
E♭
B♭
32
filled. I come guilt - y to be par - doned by the
F/A
Gm7
E♭
35
blood of Christ, the Lamb. And I'm wel - comed with
B♭/D
E♭
F

DISC 1
47
38
o - pen arms, praise God, just as I am.
Gm7
E♭
F
B♭2
mp
42
Just as I
B♭sus
B♭2
B♭sus
B♭2
46
am I would be lost, but mer - cy and
F/B♭
B♭sus
B♭2
F/B♭

50
grace my free - dom bought. And now to
E♭2/B♭
F/B♭
B♭2
54
glo - ry in Your cross, O Lamb of
B♭2/A
Gm7(4)
E♭2
B♭2/D
58
DISC 1 48
unis.
God, I come, I come.
unis.
E♭2
Fsus
F
B♭2

62
I come bro - ken to be mend - ed. I come
B♭2/A
Gm7
E♭
65
wound - ed to be healed. I come des - perate to be
B♭
F
Gm7
68
res - cued. I come emp - ty to be filled. I come
mel.
F/A

71
guil - ty to be par - doned by the blood of Christ the
Gm7 E♭ B♭/D
74
unis.
mel.
Lamb. And I'm wel - comed with o - pen arms, praise
unis.
E♭ F Gm7
DISC 1 49 DISC 1 50
PRAISE TEAM ad lib to the end
77
1.
(page 57, meas. 63)
God, just as I am. I come
E♭ F B♭ B♭sus

81
2.
p
am.
Praise
God,
just
2.
Gm7
E♭2
84
pp
as
I
am.
F
B♭2
p
pp
87
B♭sus
B♭
B♭sus
B♭
rit.

Blessings

Words and Music by
LAURA STORY
Arranged by Cliff Duren

8
tec - tion while we sleep.
We pray for heal - ing,
A♭2(no3) E♭2(no3) E♭2 F Gm7
10
DISC 1 53
for pros - per - i - ty.
We pray for Your might - y hand to
E♭2 F Dm E♭2 F Gm7
12
3
ease our suf - fer - ing.
And all the while You
F/A B♭/D E♭2
mp
14
DISC 1 54
hear each spo - ken need,
yet love is way too much to give us
Fsus F Gm9 Cm7 B♭maj7/D

16
mp
less-er things. 'Cause what if Your bless - ings come through rain-drops? What if Your heal-
CHOIR
mp
What if Your bless - ings come through rain-drops? What if Your heal-
Fsus F B♭(no3) B♭2(no3) B♭
mp
18
- ing comes through tears? What if a thou - sand sleep - less nights are what it takes
- ing comes through tears? What if a thou - sand sleep - less nights are what it takes
F/A F2/A F/A Gm9 B♭maj7/D B♭/D

DISC 1 55
20
to know You're near?
And what if trials of this life
to know You're near?
Ooo
E♭2(no3) E♭2(♯4) E♭2
Cm7 B♭/D B♭maj7/D
mf
mp
DISC 1 56
22
are Your mer - cies in dis - guise?
unis.
Are Your mer - cies in dis - guise?
unis.
E♭2(no3) Fsus
Cm B♭ F2(no3)/A F/A

24
We pray for wis - dom,
We pray for wis - dom,
E♭ Fsus Dm E♭2(no3) F Gm7
mp
26
Your voice to hear. And we cry in an - ger when we can-
Your voice to hear. We cry in an - ger when we can-
E♭2(no3) F Dm E♭2(no3) F Gm7

28
- not feel You near. We doubt Your good - ness.
- not feel You near. We doubt Your good - ness.
A♭2(no3) E♭2(no3) E♭ F Gm7
mf
DISC 1
57
30
We doubt Your love, as if ev - 'ry prom - ise from Your Word
We doubt Your love, as if ev - 'ry prom - ise from Your Word
E♭2 F Dm E♭ F Gm7

32
building
is not e-nough. And all the while You hear
is not e-nough. And all the while.
F/A
B♭/D
E♭2(no3)
building
34
DISC 1 58
each des-perate plea, and long that we'd have faith to be-
Ooo
Fsus F Gm7 Cm7 B♭/D

36
mf
lieve.___ 'Cause what if Your bless - ings come through rain - drops? What if Your heal-
mf
What if Your bless - ings come through rain - drops? What if Your heal-
Fsus F F7sus B♭
mf
38
- ing comes through tears? And what if a thou - sand sleep - less nights are what it takes
- ing comes through tears? What if a thou - sand sleep - less nights are what it takes
F/A Gm7 B♭maj7/D

40
to know You're near?
And what if trials of this life
unis.
to know You're near?
And what if trials of this life
unis.
E♭2(no3)
Cm7
B♭maj7
D
DISC 1
59
42
are Your mer - cies in dis - guise?
are Your mer - cies in dis - guise?
E♭2(no3)
F7sus
B♭sus
B♭

44
When friends be-tray us, when dark-ness seems_ to win, we know
Cm7
B♭maj7/D
E♭
Fsus
F
DISC 1
60
46
that pain re minds this heart that this is not, this is not_ our home!
This is not, this is not_ our home!
Cm7
B♭maj7/D
E♭2
Fsus
F

48
DISC 1
61
It's not our home.
Cm
B♭
F/A
E♭
F
Dm
50
slight rit.
'Cause what if Your bless-
mf
slight rit.
f
Not our home.
What if Your bless-
E♭2(no3)
F
Gm7
A♭2(no3)
Fsus
slight rit.

52
a tempo
- ings come through rain - drops? What if Your heal -
a tempo
- ings come through rain - drops? What if Your heal -
B♭
a tempo

53
- ing comes through tears? And what if a thou - sand sleep-less nights are what it takes
- ing comes through tears? What if a thou - sand sleep-less nights are what it takes
F/A
Gm7
B♭maj7/D

55
mp
— to know You're near? What if my great - est dis - ap-point-ments, or the
— to know You're near?
E♭2(no3)
B♭
mp
DISC 1
62
57
ach - ing of — this life, is a re-veal - ing of — a great-er thirst this
F/A
Gm7
B♭maj7/D

59
world can't sat-is-fy? And what if trials of this life,
mp
And what if trials of this life.
E♭2(no3)
B♭sus
C
B♭maj7
D
61
the rain, the storms, the hard-est nights are Your
E♭2(no3)
F
E♭2(no3)
G

DISC 1
63
mer-cies in disguise?
F
A
Cm
B♭
F2(no3)
A
F
A
E♭
Fsus
Dm
p
molto rit.
Ooo
Ooo
Ooo
Cm
B♭
F2(no3)
A
F
A
E♭
Fsus
F
B♭
molto rit.

I Will Rise

Words and Music by
CHRIS TOMLIN, JESSE REEVES,
LOUIE GIGLIO and MATT MAHER
Arranged by Travis Cottrell

9
an-chor for my soul. I can say, "It is well."
Fm7
D♭2
A♭2
12
Je - sus has o - ver-come, and the grave
E♭sus
A♭(no3)
A♭2
E♭/G
E♭2/G
15
is o - ver-whelmed. The vic - to - ry is won.
Fm7
D♭
D♭2
A♭/C
DISC 1
65
18
He is ris - en from the dead. And I will rise
E♭/G
Fm7
D♭2

21
when He calls my name, no more sor - row, no
CHOIR
mp
Ooo
Ooo
A♭
E♭
Fm7
24
more pain. I will rise on ea - gles' wings, be-fore
Ooo
D♭2
D♭
A♭
E♭

27
— my God fall on — my knees, and rise. —
Ooo —
Rise. —
Fm7
D♭2
D♭
A♭/C
DISC 1
66
30
— I will rise. —
—
Rise. —
mf unis.
There's a
mel.
D♭2
A♭/E♭
E♭(no3)

33
CHOIR
day that's draw - ing near, when this dark-ness breaks to light.
Fm
D♭
A♭
mf
36
unis.
And the shad - ows dis - ap - pear, and my faith
E♭sus
E♭
Fm
D♭
39
unis.
shall be my eyes. Je - sus has o - ver-come,
A♭
E♭
A♭

42
and the grave is o - ver - whelmed.
E♭
Fm
DISC 1
67
44
unis.
The vic - to - ry is won. He is
D♭2
A♭
E♭/G
E♭2/G
E♭/G
47
ris - en from the dead. And I will rise
mel.
Fm7
A♭maj7/E♭
D♭2

49
when He calls my name, no
A♭
E♭
51
more sor - row, no more pain. I will rise
Fm
D♭
53
on ea - gles' wings; be-fore my God fall on
A♭
E♭
Fm

56
my knees, and rise.
D♭maj7
A♭/C
DISC 1
68
58
I will rise.
D♭
A♭/E♭
E♭
61
f unis.
And I hear the voice of man - y an - gels sing, "Wor-
unis.
D♭
A♭
E♭
f

64
- thy is the Lamb." And I hear the cry
D♭ A♭ E♭ E♭sus E♭
DISC 1 69
66
of ev - 'ry long - ing heart, "Wor - thy is the Lamb."
D♭ A♭ E♭ D♭ A♭
69
mel.
And I hear the voice of man - y an -
E♭ E♭sus E♭ D♭ A♭
f

71
- gels sing, "Wor - thy is the Lamb."
E♭ D♭ A♭
73
And I hear the cry of ev - 'ry long-
E♭ E♭sus E♭ D♭ A♭
75
- ing heart, "Wor - thy is the Lamb." "Wor-
E♭ E♭/F Fm D♭ A♭ E♭ E♭sus E♭

DISC 1
70
78
- thy is the Lamb."
D♭
A♭
E♭
81
mp
unis.
Wor - thy, wor - thy, wor - thy is the
unis.
A♭
E♭/G
Fm7
mp
84
Lamb. Wor - thy, wor - thy,
D♭2
A♭2
E♭/G

DISC 1 71

87
PRAISE TEAM
I will rise
CHOIR
wor - thy is the Lamb.
Fm
D♭2
89
when He calls my name, no
Wor - thy, wor - thy,
A♭
E♭

91
more sor - row, no more pain. I will rise
wor - thy is the Lamb.
Fm
D♭2
93
on ea - gles' wings, be - fore
Wor - thy, wor - thy,
A♭
E♭

95
— my — God — fall on — my — knees, — and rise.
wor - thy is the Lamb.
Fm
D♭2
97
I will — rise.
I will rise.
A♭/C
D♭2

99
I will rise.
I will rise.
A♭/E♭
D♭/F
DISC 1
72
101
A♭/E♭
E♭sus

DISC 1 73

105
f
Rise!
I will rise!
A♭/C
D♭
A♭/E♭
f
108
f
I will rise when He calls
I will rise!
D♭/F
A♭/C

DISC 1
74
110
my name,
no more sor - row or pain.
I will rise!
D♭2
A♭
E♭
112
Wor - thy, wor - thy,
I will rise when He calls my name, no
D♭2
F
D♭
F
A♭
E♭

115
wor - thy is the Lamb.
Wor - thy,
more sor - row, no more pain. I will rise on ea -
Fm7
D♭2
D♭
A♭
DISC 1
75
118
wor - thy,
wor - thy is the
- gles' wings, be - fore my God fall on
E♭
Fm7

120
Lamb.
I will rise when He calls
my knees. and rise.
D♭
A♭/C
122
my name,
no more sor - row or pain.
I will rise.
D♭
A♭/E♭

124
I will rise.
I will
D♭/F
A♭/E♭
E♭
127
rit.
rise!
I will rise!
D♭2
D♭
A♭

Your Great Name

Words and Music by
KRISSY NORDHOFF
and MICHAEL NEALE
Arranged by Cliff Duren

13
feel no shame at the sound
Gm
E♭
DISC 1
78
15
of Your great name. Ev - 'ry
B♭
F
17
fear has no place at the sound
Gm7
E♭
p
19
of Your great name. The en - e-my,
B♭
Dm7

21
he has to leave at the sound
Gm
E♭
DISC 1
79
23
of Your great name.
B♭
F
CHOIR and SOLOIST
25
mp
Je - sus, worth - y is the Lamb that was
E♭
B♭
F
Gm7

27
slain for us. The Son of God and man, You are
E♭ B♭ F Gm7
29
high and lift-ed up, and all the world will praise Your great
E♭ B♭ Gm7 F
31
name. Your great
E♭ B♭ F

DISC 1
80
33
mf
— name.
All the
E♭
B♭
F
35
— weak
find their — strength
at the sound
Gm7
E♭2
mf
37
— of Your great — name.
Hun - gry
B♭
F

39
SOLOIST may ad lib
— souls re - ceive — grace at the sound
Gm7
E♭2
DISC 1
81
41
— of Your great — name. The fa - ther-less,
B♭
F
43
building
— they find their — rest — at the sound
Gm7
E♭2
building

45
of Your great name. The sick are healed
B♭
Dm
47
and the dead are raised at the sound
Gm7
E♭2
DISC 1
82
49
of Your great name!
B♭
F

51
f
Je - sus, worth - y is the Lamb that was
E♭ B♭ F Gm7
f
53
slain for us. The Son of God and man, You are
E♭ B♭ F Gm7
55
high and lift - ed up, and all the world will praise Your great
E♭ B♭ Gm7 F

57
name.
Your great
E♭
B♭
F
DISC 1
83
59
name.
E♭
B♭
F
61
ff
Re-deem-er, my Heal-er, Lord Al-might-y.
F
Gm
E♭
Gm/F
F
ff

63
My Sav - ior, De - fend - er, You are my King.
F Gm E♭ Gm/F F
65
Re - deem - er, my Heal - er, Lord Al - might - y.
F Gm E♭ Gm/F F
DISC 1
84
67
My Sav - ior, De - fend - er, You are my King.
F Gm E♭ Gm/F F

SOLO
mf
69
Je - sus, worth - y is the Lamb that was
E♭ B♭ F Gm7
mp
DISC 1
85
71
slain for us. The Son of God and man,
CHOIR
mf
You are
E♭ B♭ F Gm7
73
high and lift-ed up and all the world will praise Your great
building
E♭ B♭ Gm7 F
building

DISC 1
86
75
name.
E♭
B♭
F
77
ff
Je - sus, worth - y is the Lamb that was
F
C
E
G
Am
ff
p
ff
79
slain for us. The Son of God and man, You are
F
C
G
Am

DISC 1
87
81
(no breath)
high and lift - ed up and all the world will praise
F C Am7 G
83
Je - sus, worth - y is the Lamb that was
F C G Am
85
slain for us. The Son of God and man, You are
F C G Am G F

87
high and lift-ed up___ and all the world will praise Your great
F C Am G
DISC 1
88
89
___ name.___ Your great
F C G Em
91
___ name.___ Your great
F C G Am G

93
rit.
name.
Your great
F
C
G
rit.

95
name!
C

Fountain of Life

with Nothing but the Blood *and* There Is a Fountain

Words and Music by
TRAVIS COTTRELL, DAVID MOFFITT
and SUE C. SMITH
Arranged by Travis Cottrell

DISC2 1 **Broadly** (♩=67)

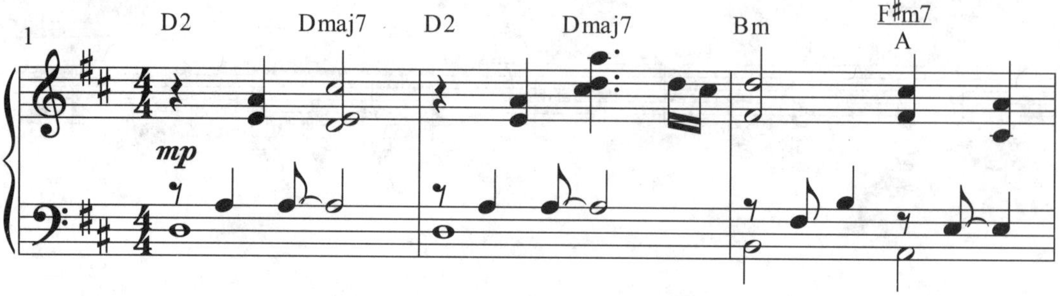

NOTHING BUT THE BLOOD (Robert Lowry)

7
that makes me white as snow.
A A/G F♯m7 Em11
DISC 2
2
10
No oth - er fount I know, noth - ing but the blood of
D D/C♯ Bm7 D/F♯ G6 D/A
13
Je - sus. O pre - cious is the flow
D D/C♯ A/C♯ Bm7
3

16
that makes me white as snow.
A A/G G F#m7 Em11 G/A
19
No oth - er fount I know, noth-ing but the blood of
D D/C# A/C# Bm7 D/F# Em/G D/A
DISC2
3
22
unis.
SOLO
Je - - sus. There
Asus A D Bm7 Esus

25 THERE IS A FOUNTAIN (William Cowper)

36
stains. And sin - ners plunged be - neath that flood lose
Esus
A
A2
D/A
A
39
DISC2 4
CHOIR
mf
all their guilt - y stains.
Dear
Dmaj7
E
A
Asus
42
dy - ing Lamb, Thy pre - cious blood shall nev - er lose its
A
D/A
A
F♯m7
mf

45
pow'r till all the ran - somed church of God be
Bm7 A D/A A
48
DISC2 5
ff
saved to sin no more. Be
A/D E A/E D2 D E
50
unis.
saved to sin no more, be saved to sin no
A E/A A D/A F♯m7
ff

53
unis.
more. Till all the ran - somed
unis.
Esus
A
55
church of God be saved to sin no
D/A
A
Bm/A
A/D
E
A/E
DISC2
6
57
more.
Foun-tain of Life,
Asus
A

59
all of my shame
bur-ied with Christ,
E
E7/G♯
A
61
oh, praise His name!
Guilt-y, I fall;
E
E7/G♯
F♯m
63
for-giv-en, I rise!
Grate-ful for-ev-
D
E7/G♯
A

DISC2 7
65
1.
SOLOISTS may start ad libs
(page 117, meas. 59)
- er, Foun-tain of Life! Foun-tain of Life,
1.
D
A
(page 117, meas. 59)
67
2.
- er, Foun-tain of Life!
2.
D
A
G
D
F♯
DISC2 8
70
rit.
unis.
E'er
Dm
F
E♭
F
rit.

72
a tempo
unis.
unis.
since by faith I saw the stream Thy flow - ing wounds sup -
B♭
E♭/B♭
B♭
Gm7
a tempo
75
ply, re - deem - ing love has been my theme, and
Cm7
B♭
E♭/B♭
B♭/A♭
E♭/G
B♭/F
78
DISC2
9
die!
ff
shall be till I die, un - til I die! And
die!
B♭/E♭
F
B♭/F
E♭2
F

81
shall be till I die, and shall be till I
B♭ F/B♭ B♭ E♭/B♭ F/B♭ E♭/B♭ Gm7 E♭/G Gm7
ff
84
die! Re - deem - ing love has
Fsus F B♭/F B♭ B♭2 B♭
86
DISC2 10
been my theme, and shall be till I
E♭/B♭ B♭ Cm/B♭ B♭/E♭ F B♭/F

88
DUET
Sop.
Foun-tain of Life.
Ten.
CHOIR
die! Foun-tain of Life, all of my shame
B♭
F
F7/A
90
All of my shame
bur-ied with Christ,
bur-ied with Christ, oh, praise His name!
B♭
F
F7/A

92
praise His name!
Guilt - y, I fall; for - giv - en, I rise.
Gm
E♭
F7
A
94
I rise. So grate - ful.
Grate - ful for - ev - er, Foun - tain of Life!
B♭
E♭

96
Guilt - y, I fall; I rise!
Guilt - y, I fall; for - giv - en, I rise!
B♭ E♭ F/A B♭
DISC2
11
99
I'm so grate - ful.
Grate - ful for - ev - er,
E♭/B♭ B♭ Cm/B♭ Cm/E♭ E♭

101
Oh, praise His
Fountain of Life!
O Fountain of Life!
E♭/G
B♭
103
name.
I'm so grateful
Fountain of Life!
Fountain of Life!
O Fountain of Life!
B♭/E♭
E♭
B♭

DISC2 12
105
Yes, I am, Lord. Yes, I am Lord. My Foun-tain of Life!
Yes, I am, Lord. There is a Foun-tain of Life!
Foun-tain of Life!
There is a Foun-tain of Life!
B♭/E♭
E♭
B♭
107
rit. .
Foun-tain of Life!
Life!
rit.
Foun-tain of Life!
E♭
E♭/G
B♭
rit.

Blood of Jesus Be My All

Words and Music by
TRAVIS COTTRELL, DAVID MOFFITT
and SUE C. SMITH
Arranged by Travis Cottrell

9
way my sin? What can cov-er ev - 'ry stain,
Fm7 E♭/G A♭2 D♭maj7 E♭
12
flood the dark-ness deep with - in
Fm9 Fm E♭/G
14
like heal - ing rain? What can make the
A♭ D♭2 D♭ E♭sus E♭(no3)

17
bro - ken whole? What can set the
Fm7 E♭/G A♭
19
cap - tive free? What can sat - is -
D♭maj7 E♭ Fm7
21
DISC2 15
fy my soul, my deep - est need?
Fm E♭/G A♭ D♭ E♭sus

24
Blood of Je - sus, be my all, all my
A♭
E♭/G
27
hope and righ - teous-ness. In Your mer - cy let me fall
B♭m
A♭/C
D♭
A♭
30
on Your grace and noth - ing less. Hear this
E♭/G
B♭m
A♭/C
D♭

DISC2
16
33
unis.
sin - ner call.
Blood of Je - sus, be my all.
unis.
E♭ Fm D♭maj7 E♭
36
Oh, the rich - es
A♭sus A♭
38
that were spilled to re-store me to my King.
Fm E♭/G A♭ D♭maj7 E♭

41
No more fear and no more guilt,
Fm
E♭/G
43
I am re-deemed. When I'm fin-ished
A♭ D♭2 E♭sus E♭
46
with this life and I stand be-fore the throne,
Fm E♭/G A♭ D♭maj7 E♭

49
I will claim the blood of Christ
Fm
E♭/G
DISC2 17
51
and Christ a - lone.
A♭
D♭
E♭sus
53
f
Blood of Je - sus, be my all,
D♭/E♭
E♭
A♭
f

55
all my hope and righ - teous-ness. In Your
Eb/G
Bbm
Ab/C
Db
58
mer - cy let me fall on Your grace and noth - ing less.
Ab
Eb/G
Bbm
Ab/C
61
Hear this sin - ner call. Blood of
Db
Eb
Fm

DISC2 18
64
unis.
Je - sus, be my all, be my all,
unis.
D♭maj7
E♭
D♭2
E♭sus
67
be my all,
D♭2
E♭sus
D♭2
DISC2 19
70
be my all.
E♭sus
D♭2

72
ff
Blood of Je - sus be my all,
Esus
D/E
E
A
ff
74
all my hope and righ - teous-ness. In Your
E/G♯
Bm
A/C♯
D
77
DISC2 20
DISC2 21
mer - cy let me fall on Your grace and noth - ing less.
A
E/G♯
Bm
A/C♯

80
1.
unis.
(page 135, meas. 73)
— Hear this sin - ner call.— Blood of
unis.
1.
(page 135, meas. 73)
D E F♯m E
83
2.
— Hear this sin - ner call.— Blood of
2.
D E F♯m E
DISC2 22
86
Je - sus be— my all.— Hear this sin - ner call.
Dmaj7 E F♯m D E

89
mp unis.
Blood of Je - sus
unis.
F♯m
Dmaj7
mp
92
rit.
a tempo
be my all.
E
A
E/G♯
rit.
a tempo
95
molto rit.
Bm
A2/G♯
D
E
D/E
A
molto rit.

Revelation Song

Words and Music by
JENNIE LEE RIDDLE
Arranged by Bradley Knight

14
Sing a new song to Him who sits on
F2
C
C2/E
Gm7
DISC2 25
17
(page 138, meas. 11)
heav - en's mer - cy seat.
B♭2
F2
(page 138, meas. 11)
CHOIR and SOLOIST
19
mf
Ho - ly, ho - ly, ho - ly is the Lord God Al - might - y,
C(no3)
Gm7
mf

21
who was, and is, and is to come.
B♭2
F(no3)
23
With all cre-a - tion I sing, "Praise to the King of kings.
C(no3)
Gm7
25
You are my ev-'ry-thing, and I will a-dore You."
B♭
B♭2(♯4)
B♭
F2

DISC2
26
27
C(no3)
Gm7
B♭2
30
SOLO
mp
Clothed in rain-bows of liv-ing col-or,
F2
C(no3)
Gm7(4)
mp
33
flash - es of light-ning, rolls of thun - der,
B♭2
F2
N.C.
F E D
f

35
f
bless-ing and hon - or, strength and glo - ry and pow-er be
C2
Gm7(4)
F/A
DISC2 27
37
to You, the on - ly wise King.
B♭2
F
39
Ho - ly, ho - ly, ho - ly is the Lord God Al - might - y,
C(no3)
Gm7

41
who was, and is, and is to come.
B♭ B♭2 F2
43
With all cre-a - tion I sing, "Praise to the King of kings.
C(no3) Gm7
45
You are my ev-'ry-thing, and I will a-dore You."
B♭ F2

47
C2
Gm7(4)
DISC2 28
49
CHOIR
mp
Filled with won-der,
B♭2
F
C
mp
52
DISC2 29
awe - struck won-der
at the men - tion of Your name.
Gm7
B♭2
F2
F

55
mf
Je - sus, Your name is pow - er, breath and liv - ing wa - ter.
C
Am7
Gm7
mf
DISC2
30
57
Such a mar - velous mys - ter - y.
B♭2
F
59
Ho - ly, ho - ly, ho - ly is the Lord God Al - might - y,
D♭
A♭m7

61
who was, and is, and is to come.
C♭
G♭2 G♭ G♭2(♯4) G♭
63
With all cre-a-tion I sing, "Praise to the King of kings.
D♭
A♭m7
G♭ A♭m G♭/B♭
DISC2
31
65
unis.
You are my ev-'ry-thing, and I will a-dore You."
C♭
G♭2 G♭
G♭2 G♭2/E♭

67
(same note)
Ho - ly, ho - ly, ho - ly is the Lord God Al - might - y,
(same note)
E
Bm7
A/C♯
69
who was, and is, and is to come. Yeah, Yeah!
D
A
DISC2 32
71
With all cre-a - tion I sing, "Praise to the King of kings.
E
C♯m7
Bm7
A Bm7 A/C♯
3

73
rit.
You are my ev-'ry-thing, and I will_ a-dore You."
D
D2(#4)
D
A2 A
rit.
75
E

All to Us

Words and Music by
CHRIS TOMLIN, JESSE REEVES,
MATT MAHER and MATT REDMAN
Arranged by Cliff Duren

8
end. We are wait - ing on You, Je - sus. We be-
E♭sus E♭ D♭ A♭/C E♭/G Fm
11
DISC2 35
lieve You're all to us.
D♭ E♭sus E♭ D♭ Fm
13
CHOIR
mp
Pre-cious Cor - ner-stone, sure Foun - da - tion, You are
E♭sus E♭ D♭ A♭/C E♭/G A♭

16
faith - ful __ to the end. We are wait - ing __ on You,
D♭ A♭/C E♭sus E♭ D♭ A♭/C
DISC2 36
19
mf
Je - sus. __ We be-lieve You're all to us. Let the
E♭/G Fm D♭ E♭sus E♭ A♭sus A♭
22
glo - ry of Your name be the pas - sion of the church. Let the
A♭
mf

24
righ-teous-ness of God be a ho - ly flame that burns. Let the
E♭ D♭2 A♭
26
sav - ing love of Christ be the meas-ure of our lives. We be -
E♭ Fm7 D♭2
28
unis.
DISC2
37
lieve You're all to us.
unis.
A♭/E♭ E♭ D♭ Fm
mp

30
mf
On - ly Son of God, sent from
E♭sus E♭ D♭ A♭/C
mf
32
unis.
heav - en, hope and mer - cy at the
E♭/G A♭ D♭ A♭/C
34
building
unis.
cross, You are ev - 'ry-thing, You're the
unis.
E♭sus E♭ D♭ A♭/C

DISC2
38
36
Prom - ise. Je - sus, You are all to
E♭/G
Fm
D♭
E♭
38
f
us! Let the glo - ry of Your name be the
A♭
A♭/C
E♭
f
40
pas - sion of the church. Let the righ - teous-ness of God be a
D♭2
A♭
E♭

42
ho - ly flame that burns. Let the sav - ing love of Christ be the
D♭2
A♭
E♭
44
meas - ure of our lives. We be - lieve You're all to
Fm7
D♭2
A♭/E♭
E♭
DISC2 39
46
us. You're
A♭
3
A♭sus
A♭
A♭/C

48
all to us! You're all to
D♭2 Fm7 E♭ A♭/C D♭2 Fm7
51
DISC2 41 2nd time
us! You're all to
E♭ A♭/C B♭m7 A♭/C
53
1.
unis.
DISC2 40
(page 156, meas. 48)
us! You are! You're
unis.
1.
(page 156, meas. 48)
D♭2 E♭ E♭7sus A♭ E♭ E♭/G A♭ A♭/C

56
2.
unis.
molto rit.
ff
us! You are! When this
unis.
unis.
D♭2 E♭ F F/E♭ B♭2/D B♭/D Dm7
molto rit.
59
a tempo
unis.
pass - ing world is o - ver, we will
unis.
E♭ B♭/D Cm7 B♭ F/A B♭ B♭/D
ff a tempo
61
see You face to face. And for -
unis.
E♭ B♭/D E♭2 Fsus F B♭/D

63
unis.
ev - er we will wor - ship. Je - sus.
E♭ B♭/D Cm7 B♭ F/A Gm
DISC2 42
65
You are all to us! Let the
E♭ F B♭ B♭/D
67
glo - ry of Your name be the pas - sion of the church. Let the
F E♭2 B♭

69
righ-teous-ness of God be a ho - ly flame that burns. Let the
F
E♭2
B♭
71
sav - ing love of Christ be the meas-ure of our lives. We be-
F
Gm7
E♭2
73
lieve You're all to us. Je - sus,
B♭/F
F
Gm7
E♭2

DISC2
43
75
You are all to us. You're
unis.
B♭/F
F
B♭
B♭/D
77
all to us! You are!
Cm7
B♭/D
E♭2
Fsus
79
rit.
E♭
Gm7
F/A
B♭
fff
rit.

In God We Still Trust

Words and Music by
KIM NASH, BILL NASH
and ROBERT LeCLAIR
Arranged by Harold Ross

10
there from the ___ be-gin - ning; that's how we've come this far. Our
E♭ B♭ B♭/D E♭2
DISC2 45
12
faith in Him through-out our his - t'ry made us who we are.
Cm7 E♭2 F
14
mf
You place your hand ___ on His Bi - ble when you
E♭/B♭ B♭

DISC2
46
16
swear to tell the truth. His name is on our great-est mon - u-ments, and
Cm/B♭ B♭ E♭/B♭ B♭
18
all our mon-ey too. And when we pledge al-le - giance, there's
CHOIR
mp
Ooo Ooo
F Fsus F E♭/B♭ B♭

20
no doubt where we stand. There's no sep-a-ra - tion; we're one na-
Ah
B♭/D
E♭2
Cm7
DISC2
47
22
f
- tion un - der Him.
In God we still
f
In God we still
E♭2
F

24
trust, here in A - mer - i - ca. He's the one we turn
trust, here in A - mer - i - ca.
B♭ B♭/D E♭2
f
26
to ev-'ry time the go - in' gets rough. He is the
3
Ooo go - in' gets rough.
B♭ B♭/D Fsus F

28
source of all our strength, the One who watch-es o - ver
unis.
Ah
watch-es o - ver
unis.
Gm
F
B♭/F
E♭
DISC2
48
30
us. Here in A - mer-i-ca, in God we still
unis.
us. Here in A - mer-i-ca, in God we still
unis.
C
Cm7
F7sus

32
ff
trust.
Now
there are those a - mong us
who
trust.
B♭
A♭
34
DISC2
49
want to push Him out
and e - rase His name
from ev-'ry-thing
this
B♭
E♭
G
A♭

36
coun-try's all — a-bout. From the school-house to the court-house they're
CHOIR
Ah
B♭ E♭ B♭/D Cm B♭/D
38
si-lenc-ing — His Word. Now it's time for all be-liev-ers — to
CHOIR
Ah
E♭ N.C. A♭ B♭/A♭ A♭

40
make our voic - es heard.
It's time to
Fsus
F
B♭
Dm7
Gm7
B♭maj7/F
E♭2
42
ff
make our voic - es heard.
In God we still
ff
In God we still
E♭/F
E/F♯

44
trust, here in A-mer-i-ca. He's the one we turn
trust, here in A-mer-i-ca.
B
B/D♯
E2
ff
46
to ev-'ry time the go-in' gets rough. He is the
3
Ooo go-in' gets rough.
B
B/D♯
F♯sus
F♯

DISC2
51
48
source of all our strength; the One who watch-es o - ver
unis.
Ah
watch-es o - ver
G♯m
F♯
B/F♯
E
50
us. Here in A-mer-i-ca, in God we still
unis.
us. Here in A-mer-i-ca, in God we still
unis.
C♯
C♯m7
F♯7sus

52
trust. Here in A-mer-i-ca, here in A-
unis.
trust. Here in A-mer-i-ca, here in A-
unis.
B
B/D♯
E2
54
mer-i-ca, here in A-mer-i-ca,
mer-i-ca, here in A-mer-i-ca,
C♯
C♯/E♯
C♯m7
B/D♯
E
G♯m

DISC2 52
56
in God we still trust.
in God we still trust.
E/F♯
B D♯m7 G♯m7 Bmaj7/F♯ E2
58
rit.
A-mer - i - ca!
rit.
A-mer - i - ca!
G/B
A/B
rit.
B
fff

Statement of Faith

Words and Music by
WES TUTTLE
Arranged by Marty Hamby

DISC2 66 **Optional Version (without narration)**

DISC2 53 **Broadly** (♩=63)

10
He a - lone is worth - y of our praise.
Gm
B♭maj7 / F
Gm / E
F / E♭
Dm
12
LADIES
ALL
Fath - er, Spir - it, Son, the Ho - ly Three in One, He
Gm
Dm
DISC2
55
14
reigns no mat - ter what the world may say.
Gm
C7sus
C7
E♭ / F
F / E♭

16
Sure - ly time has come for us to take a stand and
MEN
Bb/D
Ebm6/C
Bb2
Bb
18
LADIES
hold to our __ con - vic - tions with - out shame. Op -
Bb/D
D+
D7
Eb
Eb+
Cm/Eb
20
ALL
po - sers of __ the faith a - bound on ev - 'ry hand, but the
Cm7
C13(b9)/E
E°7
Bb/F
F2/A
Gm

DISC2
56
22
Gos - pel must be fear - less - ly pro - claimed.
Gm7
C
C7
E♭
F
24
f
I be - lieve that Je - sus is the
F7
B♭
B♭
D
mf
26
Ho - ly Son of God. He came to earth and lived a per - fect
F
E♭
E♭
Gm7
D
Cm7
F
E♭

28
life.
I be - lieve He bled and died up -
B♭/D
Cm/A
D7(♭9)
Gm
Gm(maj7)
DISC2
57
30
on a cru - el cross, and there He made the great - est sac - ri -
Gm7
B♭/C
C7
32
fice.
I be - lieve He rose a - gain and
Cm7/F
F
B♭
B♭sus/C
B♭/D

34
that He lives to - day,
and soon He's com - ing back to earth a -
F/E♭ E♭ B♭maj7/D Cm7 E♭maj7/B♭ Cm/A D7/F♯ F♯°7
36
gain.
More than just a creed,
Gm2 Gm Fm7(4) B♭/D E♭ F/E♭ E♭maj7 C13(♭9)/E E°7
38
this is what I be - lieve:
Je - sus is the on - ly
B♭/F D/F♯ Gm Gm7 Cm7 D+ D7

DISC2
58
40
way. This is my state-ment of faith.
Fm6/A♭ G7 B°7 Cm B♭/D Cm/E♭ Gm/E F E♭/B♭ B♭ E♭m6/F
SOLO
mf
43
I be-lieve the Bi - ble is the Word of God
B♭2 E♭m6/B♭ B♭ F/A
mf
45
giv - en to the world to show the way. No
Gm B♭/F Gm/E F/E♭ Dm

47
room for com-pro-mise on its trust-wor-thi-ness, it's
Gm
Dm
49
here for us to fol - low and o - bey.
Gm
C7sus
C7
E♭/F
F/E♭
51
There are ab - so-lutes that can-not be de-nied, and
B♭/D
E♭m6/C
B♭2
B♭

53
what is true for - ev - er shall re - main. I
B♭/D D+ D7 E♭ B♭6/D
55
made my choice to live for Christ the cru - ci-fied, the
Cm7 C13(♭9)/E E°7 B♭/F F2/A Gm
DISC2 59
57
liv-ing One who is the on-ly way.
Gm7/C C7 A♭ F7

SOLOIST continue with choir
60
f
I be-lieve that Je-sus is the Ho-ly Son of God. He
B♭ B♭/D F/E♭ E♭ Gm7/D
62
came to earth and lived a per-fect life.
Cm7 F/E♭ B♭/D Cm/A D7(♭9)
64
I be-lieve He bled and died up-on a cru-el cross, and
Gm Gm(maj7) Gm7

DISC2
60
Optional Version to 𝄋
(page 189, meas. 109)
66
there He made the great - est sac - ri - fice.
Optional Version to 𝄋
(page 189, meas. 109)
B♭/C
C7
Cm7/F
F
68
I be-lieve He rose a-gain and that He lives to-day, and
B♭
B♭sus/C
B♭/D
F/E♭
E♭
B♭maj7/D
Cm7
E♭maj7/B♭
70
soon He's com - ing back to earth a - gain.
Cm/A
D7/F♯
F♯°7
Gm2
Gm
Fm7(4)
B♭/D

72
3
More than just a creed, this is what I be-lieve:
3
E♭ F/E♭ E♭maj7 C13(♭9)/E E°7 B♭/F D/F♯ Gm Gm7
74
Je - sus is the on - ly way.
Cm7 D+ D7 Fm6/A♭ G7 B°7
DISC2
61
76
This is my state - ment of faith.
Cm B♭/D Cm/E♭ Gm/E F E♭/D♭ B♭

I believe in God, the only true God and in His Son Jesus Christ.

I believe that Jesus is the Word made flesh and that through God the Father all things were made.

For our salvation and by the power of the Holy Spirit, Jesus was born of the virgin Mary.

He walked on this earth, lived blameless and without sin. He came as a servant, healing the lame, …

… the blind, and the deaf, and also raising the dead.

I believe Jesus died on a cross as the ultimate sacrifice for all people, and that His death erases the debt of sin for all who believe in Him.

And whoever believes in Him will not die, but will live forever.

I believe in the resurrection of Christ. Though He suffered and was buried, on the third day …

… He rose from the dead conquering hell and the grave.

He ascended into heaven, where He has prepared a place for us to live with Him eternally.

I believe in the church, God's body of believers, charged with spreading the Good News throughout the world.

I believe in the Holy Spirit, the breath of God, who lives in every believer. The Spirit illuminates truth and inspires …

… believers to worship and to serve Jesus Christ.

He is our Helper, our Comfort and our Compass.

I believe that Jesus will come again to judge both the living and the dead, and that His kingdom will have no end. He is Lord of lords, King of kings, Creator of heaven and earth who reigns now and forever. Hallelujah!

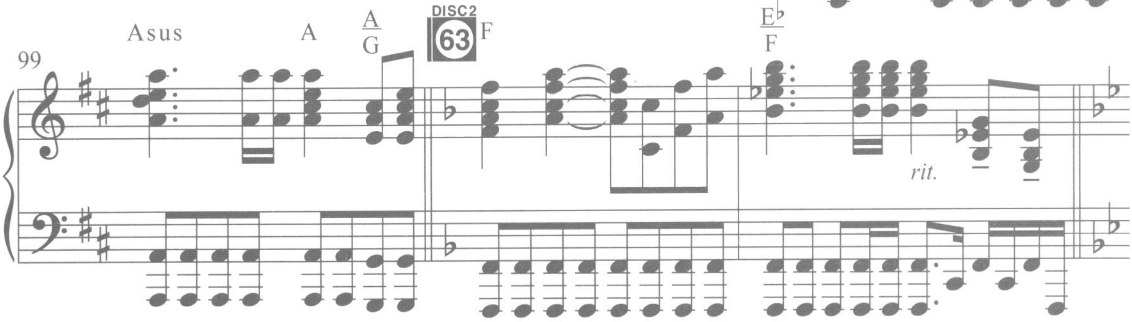

CHOIR
102
f a tempo
SOLOIST ad lib
I be-lieve that Je-sus is the Ho-ly Son of God. He
B♭ B♭/D F/E♭ E♭ B♭6/D
f a tempo
104
came to earth and lived a per-fect life.
Cm7 F/E♭ B♭/D Cm/A D7(♭9)
106
I be-lieve He bled and died up-on a cru-el cross, and
Gm Gm(maj7) Gm7

DISC2
64
108
there He made the great-est sac-ri-fice.
Gm7/C
C7
E♭/F
F/G
110
ff
unis.
I be-lieve He rose a-gain and that He lives to-day, and
C
Csus/D
C/E
G/F
F
Cmaj7/E
Dm
Fmaj7/C
112
soon He's com-ing back to earth a-gain.
Dm/B
E/G♯
G♯°7
Am2
Am
Gm7
C/D

114
More than just a creed, this is what I be-lieve:
F G/F Fmaj7 D13(♭9)/F♯ F♯°7 C/G E/G♯ Am Am7
DISC2 65
116
Je-sus is the on-ly way. This is my
Dm7 E+ E Gm6/B♭ A C♯°7 Dm C/E Dm/F

119
unis.
state - ment of faith. My state - ment of
unis.
Am/F♯ G A♭/G♭ Fm6 A♭/E♭ Fm/D Fm/G
3

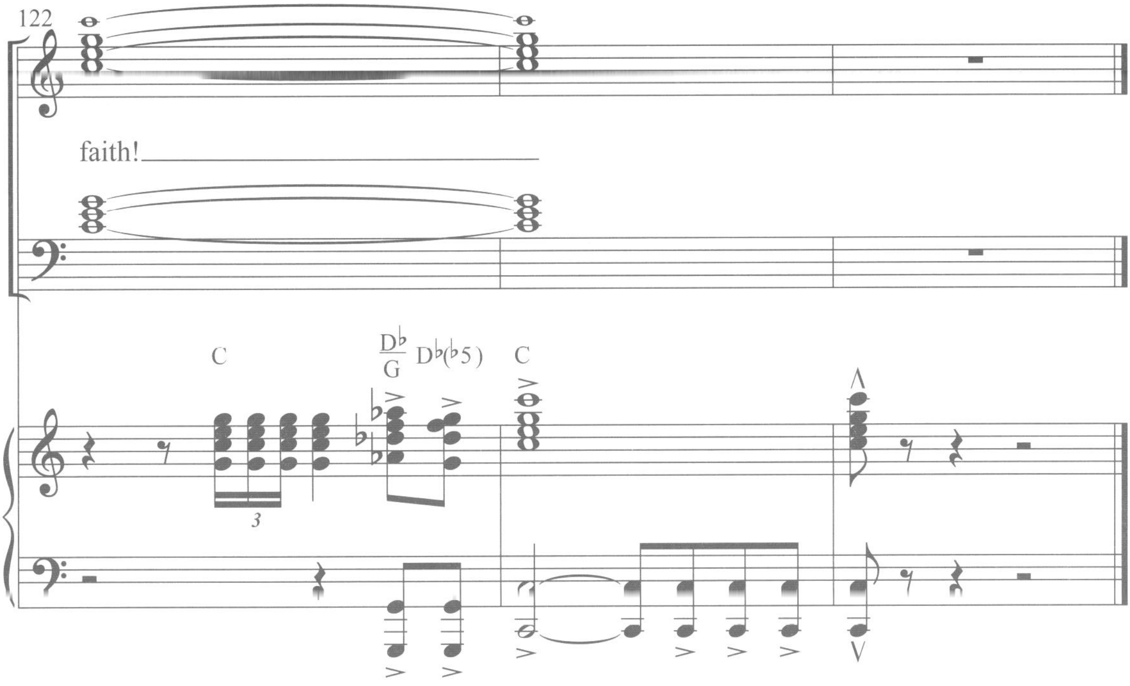
122
faith!
C D♭/G D♭(♭5) C
3

What a Lovely Name

Words and Music by
CHARLES B. WYCUFF
Arranged by Marty Hamby

17
LADIES
It's the love-ly name of Je - sus, ev-er-more the
D G D
21
DISC2
69
same, what a love-ly name.
A7 D G D
25
ALL f
What a love-ly name this name of Je - sus,
D G D
f

28
reach-ing high-er far
than the bright-est
Em
A7
31
star.
Sweet - er than the
D
G A D
3
34
songs they sing in heav - en,
let the world pro-
G
D

DISC2
70
37
2nd time to
(page 196, meas. 57)
claim, what a love-ly name.
Em
A7
D
G
D
41
DUET (or CHOIR)
He'll re - turn in clouds of glo - ry. Saints of ev-'ry
G
D
mf
45
race shall be-hold His face.
A7
D
G
A

49
With Him en-ter heav-en's cit - y, ev-er to ac-
D G D
53
DISC2 71
D.S. al Coda
(page 193, meas. 25)
claim what a love-ly name.
A7 D G D
D.S. al Coda
(page 193, meas. 25)
CODA
DISC2 72
57
name.
What a love-ly
CODA
D G D Ab/C Bb/D Eb
3

60
name this name of Je - sus,
reach-ing high - er
A♭
E♭
63
far
than the bright-est star.
Fm
B♭7
E♭
A♭ B♭
67
DISC2
73
Sweet - er than the songs they sing in heav - en,
E♭
A♭
E♭
3

70
let the world pro - claim,
ev - er - more the
Fm
B♭7
73
same,
let the world pro - claim,
pro -
Fm
B♭7
Fm
76
rit.
(6)
claim, what a love - ly name!
What a love - ly name!
B♭7
E♭
A♭
E♭
rit.